BRAIN BOOSTERS

TIMES TABLES
AND MULTIPLICATION
ACTIVITY BOOK

ARCTURUS

ARCTURUS

This edition published in 2020 by
Arcturus Publishing Limited
26/27 Bickels Yard, 151–153 Bermondsey Street,
London SE1 3HA

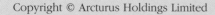
Author: Penny Worms
Illustrator and designer: Graham Rich
Consultant: Amanda Rock
Thunderpanda Font by Eric Wirjanata
www.thunderpanda.com

ISBN: 978-1-78950-243-5
CH006947NT
Supplier 29, Date 1219, Print Run 9633

Printed in China

CONTENTS

WHAT IS MULTIPLICATION?

I'm Dr. Whiskers, and this is my family.

Multiplication is a fast and clever way to find the total quantity of something without having to count or add.

Counting and adding are perfect for when you have a small amount of something.

COUNT the mice ...

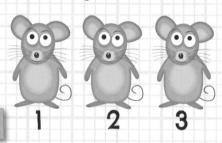

1 2 3

Three more mice arrive. You could count all the mice to find the total number, or you could

ADD the two groups together.

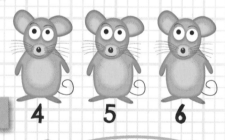

4 5 6

3 + 3 = 6

THERE'S MORE!

But what if another six mice come along? And then another six? What will you have then?

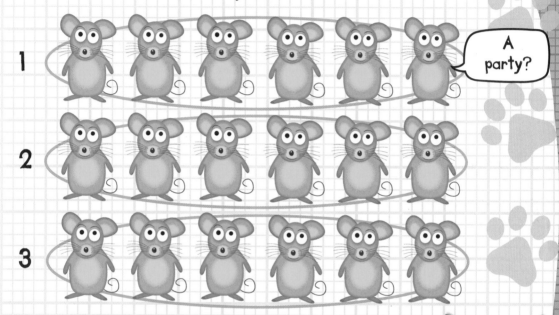

1

2

3

A party?

To find the total number of mice, you could COUNT them or ADD each group of six together. OR you could MULTIPLY them, because you have three groups of six mice.

3 x 6 = 18

And how do I know that 3 x 6 = 18? Because I know my times tables, and you will, too, by the end of this book. So just follow me, Sherlock Bones, dog detective!

WHY MULTIPLY?

Multiplication has lots of uses. Here are some.

MONEY

How much is the taxi?

We need 2 trips.

11 coins a trip.

11 x 2 = 22
So, 22 coins.

PLAYING A GAME

You get 3 points when you score.

What's 3 x 3?

I have scored 3 times.

I have 9 points!

FINDING A QUANTITY

I have 5 mice coming for dinner. Can you buy me 12 slices of cheese for each.

5 x 12 = 60
I need to buy 60 slices of cheese. Plus some for me!

TELLING TIME

If the clock shows this, how many minutes after 7 is it?

There are 5 minutes between each number, so 5 x 5 = 25. It's 25 minutes after 7.

FINDING CLUES

There are different ways of saying "multiply." To find the clues that tell you what to do, learn these terms. Put an X in the box when you can remember them.

Two **MULTIPLIED BY** three

Two **TIMES** three

Two **SETS OF** three

The **PRODUCT** of two and three

Two **GROUPS OF** three

DOUBLE three

2 x 3

THEY ALL MEAN THE SAME.

And the answer is **6**!

READY FOR MORE?

NUMBER LINES

As a junior detective, you can use number lines to help you understand and learn the times tables. Here's how.

In this number line of nasty bugs, every second bug is a STINGER and every third bug is a STINKER.

Red arrows show the STINGERS.

1 2 3 4 5 6 7 8 9 10 11 12

Purple arrows show the STINKERS.

Fill in the numbers of the next three STINGERS.

STINGERS 2 4 6 ◯ ◯ ◯

Fill in the numbers of the next two STINKERS.

STINKERS 3 6 ◯ ◯

Which two bugs are both STINGERS and STINKERS? ◯ ◯

Quick! Cuff them, Dr. Whiskers!

TIMES TABLES

Look at the Stingers in the number line again. Their numbers are the start of the 2 times table. Can you fill in the gaps?

2 4 6 8 10 12 ☐ 16 ☐ 20 ☐ 24

Look at the Stinkers in the number line again. Their numbers are the start of the 3 times table. Can you fill in the gaps?

3 6 9 12 ☐ 18 ☐ 24 ☐ 30 ☐ 36

All the answers are at the end of the book.

You could count on your fingers or draw a number line.

GREAT STUFF!

TERRIFIC TIMES TABLES

Here are all the times tables up to 12. You might know some of them.

x2
1 x 2 = 2
2 x 2 = 4
3 x 2 = 6
4 x 2 = 8
5 x 2 = 10
6 x 2 = 12
7 x 2 = 14
8 x 2 = 16
9 x 2 = 18
10 x 2 = 20
11 x 2 = 22
12 x 2 = 24

x3
1 x 3 = 3
2 x 3 = 6
3 x 3 = 9
4 x 3 = 12
5 x 3 = 15
6 x 3 = 18
7 x 3 = 21
8 x 3 = 24
9 x 3 = 27
10 x 3 = 30
11 x 3 = 33
12 x 3 = 36

x4
1 x 4 = 4
2 x 4 = 8
3 x 4 = 12
4 x 4 = 16
5 x 4 = 20
6 x 4 = 24
7 x 4 = 28
8 x 4 = 32
9 x 4 = 36
10 x 4 = 40
11 x 4 = 44
12 x 4 = 48

x5
1 x 5 = 5
2 x 5 = 10
3 x 5 = 15
4 x 5 = 20
5 x 5 = 25
6 x 5 = 30
7 x 5 = 35
8 x 5 = 40
9 x 5 = 45
10 x 5 = 50
11 x 5 = 55
12 x 5 = 60

x6
1 x 6 = 6
2 x 6 = 12
3 x 6 = 18
4 x 6 = 24
5 x 6 = 30
6 x 6 = 36
7 x 6 = 42
8 x 6 = 48
9 x 6 = 54
10 x 6 = 60
11 x 6 = 66
12 x 6 = 72

x7
1 x 7 = 7
2 x 7 = 14
3 x 7 = 21
4 x 7 = 28
5 x 7 = 35
6 x 7 = 42
7 x 7 = 49
8 x 7 = 56
9 x 7 = 63
10 x 7 = 70
11 x 7 = 77
12 x 7 = 84

x8

1 x 8 = 8
2 x 8 = 16
3 x 8 = 24
4 x 8 = 32
5 x 8 = 40
6 x 8 = 48
7 x 8 = 56
8 x 8 = 64
9 x 8 = 72
10 x 8 = 80
11 x 8 = 88
12 x 8 = 96

x9

1 x 9 = 9
2 x 9 = 18
3 x 9 = 27
4 x 9 = 36
5 x 9 = 45
6 x 9 = 54
7 x 9 = 63
8 x 9 = 72
9 x 9 = 81
10 x 9 = 90
11 x 9 = 99
12 x 9 = 108

x10

1 x 10 = 10
2 x 10 = 20
3 x 10 = 30
4 x 10 = 40
5 x 10 = 50
6 x 10 = 60
7 x 10 = 70
8 x 10 = 80
9 x 10 = 90
10 x 10 = 100
11 x 10 = 110
12 x 10 = 120

x11

1 x 11 = 11
2 x 11 = 22
3 x 11 = 33
4 x 11 = 44
5 x 11 = 55
6 x 11 = 66
7 x 11 = 77
8 x 11 = 88
9 x 11 = 99
10 x 11 = 110
11 x 11 = 121
12 x 11 = 132

x12

1 x 12 = 12
2 x 12 = 24
3 x 12 = 36
4 x 12 = 48
5 x 12 = 60
6 x 12 = 72
7 x 12 = 84
8 x 12 = 96
9 x 12 = 108
10 x 12 = 120
11 x 12 = 132
12 x 12 = 144

Look at the 6 times table.
Finish this equation.

7 x 6 = 42

Look at the 7 times table.
Finish this equation.

6 x 7 = 42

You see! It doesn't matter which number comes first, the answer is the same.

11

TIMES TABLE GRID

On the opposite page is a grid showing all the times tables together. You can see the numbers 1 to 12 in the yellow row at the top and in the yellow column on the left. If you want to find the answer to 8 x 9, trace your finger along the yellow row to 8 and then down, until you get to row 9. There is your answer: 72.

Now find these answers.

9 x 8 =

6 x 3 =

12 x 11 =

7 x 1 =

10 x 6 =

12 x 2 =

Look at the numbers to the left and right of the diagonal green line. They are mirror images of each other.

IMPORTANT MESSAGE FROM SHERLOCK BONES!

There isn't a 0 times table in the grid because all the answers are 0!

	1	2	3	4	5	6	7	8	9	10	11	12
1	1	2	3	4	5	6	7	8	9	10	11	12
2	2	4	6	8	10	12	14	16	18	20	22	24
3	3	6	9	12	15	18	21	24	27	30	33	36
4	4	8	12	16	20	24	28	32	36	40	44	48
5	5	10	15	20	25	30	35	40	45	50	55	60
6	6	12	18	24	30	36	42	48	54	60	66	72
7	7	14	21	28	35	42	49	56	63	70	77	84
8	8	16	24	32	40	48	56	64	72	80	88	96
9	9	18	27	36	45	54	63	72	81	90	99	108
10	10	20	30	40	50	60	70	80	90	100	110	120
11	11	22	33	44	55	66	77	88	99	110	121	132
12	12	24	36	48	60	72	84	96	108	120	132	144

All the answers are called MULTIPLES.
72 is a multiple of 8 and 9.

LET'S START WITH 2.

13

MULTIPLY BY 2

All the answers in the 2 times table are EVEN numbers, which end in 2, 4, 6, 8, or 0. The best way to learn them is to say them out loud, over and over again.

Use the table—or cover it up—to answer these equations.

2 TIMES TABLE

$1 \times 2 = 2$
$2 \times 2 = 4$
$3 \times 2 = 6$
$4 \times 2 = 8$
$5 \times 2 = 10$
$6 \times 2 = 12$
$7 \times 2 = 14$
$8 \times 2 = 16$
$9 \times 2 = 18$
$10 \times 2 = 20$
$11 \times 2 = 22$
$12 \times 2 = 24$

$2 \times 2 =$

$5 \times 2 =$

$7 \times 2 =$

$10 \times 2 =$

$12 \times 2 =$

$1 \times 2 =$

When you times ANY number by 1, the number doesn't change.

PRACTICE TIME

x2

Time to try your 2 times table with Pip the Puffin.

Fill in the gaps in this number pattern.

2 ⬤ 6 8 10 12 ⬤ 16 18 20 22 ⬤

Now try it backwards!

24 ⬤ 20 18 16 14 ⬤ 10 8 6 4 ⬤

Pip and his Pa have had a successful fishing trip. They have caught two groups of eight fish—eight yellow and eight blue. What is the total number of fish?

A BRAINY PAIR OF PUFFINS!

MULTIPLY BY 4

Just like the 2 times table, all the answers in the 4 times table are EVEN numbers, which end in 2, 4, 6, 8, or 0. And if you look back, you'll see the answers are DOUBLE the 2 times table.

4 TIMES TABLE
1 x 4 = 4
2 x 4 = 8
3 x 4 = 12
4 x 4 = 16
5 x 4 = 20
6 x 4 = 24
7 x 4 = 28
8 x 4 = 32
9 x 4 = 36
10 x 4 = 40
11 x 4 = 44
12 x 4 = 48

Use the table—or cover it up—to answer these equations.

4 x 4 =

11 x 4 =

9 x 4 =

2 x 4 =

8 x 4 =

5 x 4 =

PRACTICE TIME

Look at the table if you need to!

x4

Help Pip with these equations.
Test yourself by covering up the table.

◯ x 4 = 28

◯ x 4 = 36

12 x 4 = ◯

10 x 4 = ◯

3 x 4 = ◯

Fill in the gaps in this number pattern.

4 8 ◯ 16 20 24 ◯ 32 36 40 ◯ 48

Can you calculate which number comes next? ☐

If you got the last one right, you know 13 x 4!

PIP, PIP HOORAY!

17

MULTIPLES OF 2 AND 4

MULTIPLES of 2 are numbers into which 2 goes exactly. So all the answers in the 2 times table are multiples of 2. And so is any EVEN number.

Remember, all even numbers end in 2, 4, 6, 8, or 0.

Circle the number that ISN'T a multiple of 2.

4   7   6   10   8   14   20   30

MULTIPLES of 4 are numbers into which 4 goes exactly. All the answers in the 4 times table are multiples of 4. They are also multiples of 2, because 4 is a multiple of 2!

Be careful. Not all even numbers are multiples of 4.

Circle the number that ISN'T a multiple of 4.

4   12   8   24   32   16   22   28

If 40 is a multiple of both 2 and 4, is 80? Yes! 80 is double 40, so it has to be.

PIP'S PUZZLE TIME

x2 x4

Pip and his Pa are playing a game, rolling stones off the cliff. They score 2 points if a stone lands on the island and 4 points if it lands in the albatross nest. Pip has added up his score. Do it for Pa to see who has won.

Score	Island (2 pts)	Nest (4 pts)	Total
Pip	1		3 2 + 12 = 14
Pa	2		2 + =

Look at these numbers.

20   6   51   44

39   16   11   28

How many are multiples of 2? ☐

How many are multiples of 4? ☐

YOU'VE CRACKED IT!

19

MULTIPLY BY 10

The 10 times table is easy to learn—even for Coco the clownfish (fish have very bad memories). Look at the answers. They are all the original numbers with a zero added.

Use the table—or cover it up—to answer these.

10 TIMES TABLE

1 x 10 = 10
2 x 10 = 20
3 x 10 = 30
4 x 10 = 40
5 x 10 = 50
6 x 10 = 60
7 x 10 = 70
8 x 10 = 80
9 x 10 = 90
10 x 10 = 100
11 x 10 = 110
12 x 10 = 120

1 x 10 = ◯

8 x 10 = ◯

11 x 10 = ◯

2 x 10 = ◯

4 x 10 = ◯

7 x 10 = ◯

Now try this one:

13 x 10 = ◯

PRACTICE TIME

Time to practise your 10 times table with Coco the clownfish.

◯ x 10 = 120

◯ x 10 = 60

Coco has collected 10 pearls each year for 5 years. How many pearls does she have?

Fill in the gaps in this number pattern.

10 ◯ 30 ◯ 50 ◯ 70 ◯ 90 ◯ 110 ◯

Can you do this one?

100 110 120 ◯ 140 ◯ 160 ◯

The numbers go up in leaps of 10.

TIP-TOP TENS!

MULTIPLY BY 5

Odd numbers end in 1, 3, 5, 7, 9. Even numbers end in 2, 4, 6, 8, 0.

ALL the numbers in the 5 times table end in 0 or 5. If you multiply an EVEN number by 5, the answer ends in 0. If you multiply an ODD number by 5, the answer ends in 5. Simple!

Complete the equations below.

5 TIMES TABLE

$1 \times 5 = 5$
$2 \times 5 = 10$
$3 \times 5 = 15$
$4 \times 5 = 20$
$5 \times 5 = 25$
$6 \times 5 = 30$
$7 \times 5 = 35$
$8 \times 5 = 40$
$9 \times 5 = 45$
$10 \times 5 = 50$
$11 \times 5 = 55$
$12 \times 5 = 60$

$5 \times 5 =$

$3 \times 5 =$

$7 \times 5 =$

$9 \times 5 =$

$8 \times 5 =$

$4 \times 5 =$

Can you do this one?

$13 \times 5 =$

PRACTICE TIME

Now try these.

6 x 5 = ◯   2 x 5 = ◯   10 x 5 = ◯

◯ x 5 = 45   ◯ x 5 = 55   ◯ x 5 = 25

Clownfish love sea anemones. If Coco the clownfish visits five anemones a day, how many does she visit in a week? ☐

If Coco takes five minutes to swim around the coral reef, how long does it take her to swim around it three times? ☐

Complete this number pattern.

10   15   20   25   ☐   35   40   ☐

Here's a tip! The 5 times table is half the 10 times table!

GREAT! YOU KNOW YOUR FIVE TIMES TABLE!

23

x5 x10

It's the day of the great underwater carnival. Coco the clownfish is playing a game. You win a prize every time you find a multiple of 5. Help her by drawing a bubble around each one.

I've found two. Can you find eight more?

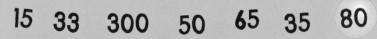

15	33	300	50	65	35	80
28	95	44	70	101	110	155	29

Five numbers are also multiples of 10. Write them in the fish below.

Remember, if you multiply an EVEN number by 5, the answer ends in 0. If you multiply an ODD number by 5, the answer ends in 5. So, can you finish the equations below?

$$202 \times 5 = \boxed{1,01....}$$

$$55 \times 5 = \boxed{27....}$$

COCO'S PUZZLE TIME

Now help Coco through the seaweed maze, picking up shells as you go.
Each orange shell scores five points. Each purple shell scores ten points.
How many points do you get in total? Fill in the equations below to find out.

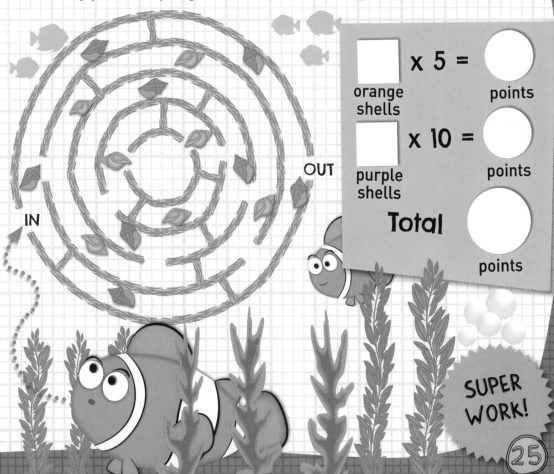

□ x 5 = ○ points
orange shells

□ x 10 = ○ points
purple shells

Total ○ points

IN

OUT

SUPER WORK!

25

MULTIPLES OF 100 AND 1,000

You know how to multiply by 10—you put a zero on the end. But let's look at what's really going on. When you know about PLACE VALUE, you'll be able to multiply by 100, 1,000, and even a million!

Did you know that the number **12** is made up of 1 ten and 2 units?

1 group of 10 fish   +   2 fish = 12 fish

You can write numbers in columns like this:

HUNDREDS	TENS	UNITS
	1	2

When you times a whole number by 10, you move all numbers to the left. The tens become hundreds, the units become tens, and there are no units.

	H	T	U
12 X 1 =		1	2
12 X 10 =	1	2	0

x 100
x 1,000

When you times a number by 100, you move all the numbers TWO places to the left and add TWO zeros. When you times a number by 1,000, it's THREE places to the left and THREE zeros.

	TEN THOUSANDS	THOUSANDS	HUNDREDS	TENS	UNITS
12 X 1 =				1	2
12 X 10 =			1	2	0
12 X 100 =		1	2	0	0
12 X 1.000 =	1	2	0	0	0

Can you fill in the answers to these equations?

	THOUSANDS	HUNDREDS	TENS	UNITS
6 X 10 =				
6 X 100 =				
6 X 1.000 =				
16 X 100 =				

WOW. YOU DID IT!

27

MULTIPLY BY 3

Remember, odd numbers end in 1, 3, 5, 7, 9. Even numbers end in 2, 4, 6, 8, 0.

Three is an odd number. If you multiply two odd numbers together, the answer is ODD. If you times an odd number by an even number, the answer is EVEN.

$1 \times 3 = 3$

odd x odd = odd

$2 \times 3 = 6$

even x odd = even

3 TIMES TABLE

$1 \times 3 = 3$
$2 \times 3 = 6$
$3 \times 3 = 9$
$4 \times 3 = 12$
$5 \times 3 = 15$
$6 \times 3 = 18$
$7 \times 3 = 21$
$8 \times 3 = 24$
$9 \times 3 = 27$
$10 \times 3 = 30$
$11 \times 3 = 33$
$12 \times 3 = 36$

Use the table—or cover it up—to answer these equations.

$3 \times 3 = $

$8 \times 3 = $

$9 \times 3 = $

$12 \times 3 = $

Read out loud the answers in the 3 times table. Can you go beyond 12?

(28)

x3

Look at these equations. Circle if the answer should be odd or even.

23 x 3 = ODD or EVEN   18 x 3 = ODD or EVEN

Flip the frog must jump from lily pad to lily pad in the order of the 3 times table. Help him by drawing arrows like the one below.

Flip can jump 3 laps in one leap. How many leaps does he take to cover 15 laps?

YOU'RE MAKING GREAT NUMBER LEAPS, TOO!

MULTIPLY BY 6

Look at the answers. The units go 6, 2, 8, 4, 0. This pattern doesn't change, so 13 x 6 ends in 8, and 14 x 6 ends in 4.

There are two things to remember about the 6 times table. Because 6 is an even number, all the answers are EVEN. And they are DOUBLE the 3 times table!

Complete the equations below.

6 TIMES TABLE

1 x 6 = 6
2 x 6 = 12
3 x 6 = 18
4 x 6 = 24
5 x 6 = 30
6 x 6 = 36
7 x 6 = 42
8 x 6 = 48
9 x 6 = 54
10 x 6 = 60
11 x 6 = 66
12 x 6 = 72

2 x 6 = ◯

4 x 6 = ◯

5 x 6 = ◯

11 x 6 = ◯

See how 7 x 6 is double 7 x 3.

7 x 3 = ◯

7 x 3 = ◯

Write the above answers here.

Now add them.

7 x 6 = ◯ + ◯ = ▢

PRACTICE TIME

Now try these.

3 x 6 = ◯   8 x 6 = ◯   12 x 6 = ◯

◯ x 6 = 24   ◯ x 6 = 42   ◯ x 6 = 54

Flip eats six bugs for his dinner every day. How many bugs does he eat in six days? ☐

How many bugs does he eat in seven days? ☐

Complete this number pattern.

6 ◯ 18 ◯ 30 42

Remember, 6, 2, 8, 4, 0.

MULTIPLY BY 9

Look at the answers below. The tens go up, 1, 2, 3, 4 ... The units go down, 9, 8, 7, 6 ...

Learning the 9 times table is easy if you know the tips and tricks—and there are many tips and tricks!

If you add together the digits in each answer (the product), they add up to 9.

9 TIMES TABLE

$1 \times 9 = 9$
$2 \times 9 = 18$
$3 \times 9 = 27$
$4 \times 9 = 36$
$5 \times 9 = 45$
$6 \times 9 = 54$
$7 \times 9 = 63$
$8 \times 9 = 72$
$9 \times 9 = 81$
$10 \times 9 = 90$
$11 \times 9 = 99$
$12 \times 9 = 108$

$7 \times 9 = 63 \quad 6 + 3 = 9$

And from 1 to 10, the first digit of the multiple (the tens) is one less than the MULTIPLIER.

$7 \times 9 = 63$

7 is the multiplier. 63 is the multiple.

So, using these tricks, complete this equation.

$9 \times 9 = \bigcirc$

PRACTICE TIME

Now cover up the times table, and complete these equations.

3 x 9 = ◯   2 x 9 = ◯   11 x 9 = ◯

◯ x 9 = 90   ◯ x 9 = 9   ◯ x 9 = 54

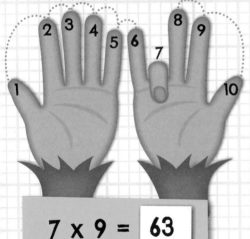

7 x 9 = **63**

Orla the orangutan is here to show you another magic way to do the 9 times table, using your 10 fingers. Imagine they are numbered 1 to 10. To times 7 by 9 (or 9 by 7), hold down the number 7 finger for the answer.

The number of fingers to the left are the tens (6). The number of fingers to the right are the units (3).

Use this method to do this equation:

4 x 9 = ▢

MULTIPLES OF 3, 6, AND 9

> All multiples of 6 and 9 are multiples of 3, because 6 and 9 are multiples of 3!

Flip is playing leapfrog again. This time, he is only allowed to jump on lily pads that are multiples of both 3 and 6. Circle the lily pads he can land on (there are four).

39   6   30   33   27   12   15   21   3   18   54   9

There is a special lily pad that is a multiple of 3, 6, and 9. Which one is it? Write the number here.

FLIP'S PUZZLE TIME

Multiples of 9 are easy to spot—the digits add up to 9.
If they add up to a double digit, keep adding.

$13 \times 9 = 117$ $1 + 1 + 7 = 9$

$21 \times 9 = 189$ $1 + 8 + 9 = 18$ $1 + 8 = 9$

Now Flip can only land on lily pads that are
multiples of 3 and 9. There are three. Circle them.

Check the times
tables grid on page 13
if you get stuck. The
numbers must appear
in both the 3 and 9
times tables.

9   33   24

27

12   55

36

28

21

Did you find the number that is a
multiple of 3, 6, and 9? Write it here.

35

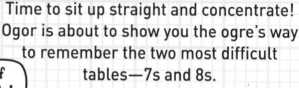

x7

MULTIPLY BY 7

Time to sit up straight and concentrate! Ogor is about to show you the ogre's way to remember the two most difficult tables—7s and 8s.

You know most of your sevens already!

With multiplication, it doesn't matter which way around the numbers go, so complete these equations.

7 TIMES TABLE

1 x 7 = 7
2 x 7 = 14
3 x 7 = 21
4 x 7 = 28
5 x 7 = 35
6 x 7 = 42
7 x 7 = 49
8 x 7 = 56
9 x 7 = 63
10 x 7 = 70
11 x 7 = 77
12 x 7 = 84

7 x 2 = ◯

2 x 7 = ◯

7 x 3 = ◯

3 x 7 = ◯

7 x 4 = ◯

4 x 7 = ◯

7 x 5 = ◯

5 x 7 = ◯

PRACTICE TIME

Time to memorize the hard ones.
Complete these equations by COPYING from the times table.

6 x 7 = ◯   7 x 7 = ◯   8 x 7 = ◯

Now COVER UP the rest of the page, and complete the equations.
Say them out loud as you do them.

6 x 7 = ◯   7 x 7 = ◯   8 x 7 = ◯

Now complete this number pattern.

7 ◯ 21 28 ◯ 42 ◯ 56 63 ◯ 77 84

Jump 7 each time.
Use your ten skinny human
fingers if you need to.

MULTIPLY BY 8

Here's the best way to remember 8 x 8: "I ate (8) and ate (8) till I was sick on the floor (64)!"

Since 8 is an even number, you know that all the answers are EVEN. And also, the 8 times table is DOUBLE the 4 times table. This could help you.

Complete these equations.

8 TIMES TABLE

1 x 8 = 8
2 x 8 = 16
3 x 8 = 24
4 x 8 = 32
5 x 8 = 40
6 x 8 = 48
7 x 8 = 56
8 x 8 = 64
9 x 8 = 72
10 x 8 = 80
11 x 8 = 88
12 x 8 = 96

5 x 8 = ◯
5 x **EVEN** ends in 0

2 x 8 = ◯

Remember the tips for 9s? The multiple starts with one less than the multiplier, and the digits add up to 9.

9 x 8 = ◯
8 is the multiplier

Now do these.

3 x 4 = ◯

3 x 4 = ◯

Write the above answers here.   Now add them.

3 x 8 = ◯ + ◯ = ◯

(38)

PRACTICE TIME

Time to put it all into practice. Cover up the times table, and complete these equations.

6 x 8 = ◯   7 x 8 = ◯   12 x 8 = ◯

◯ x 8 = 24   ◯ x 8 = 88   ◯ x 8 = 64

Now complete this number pattern by filling in the units.

8	16	2...	3...	4...	4...	5...	6...	7...	8...

Ogor has eight boots. Each boot has two holes. How many holes does he have?

If it costs 8 pennies to fix one boot, how much will it cost to fix all eight boots?

How much?!

39

MULTIPLES OF 7 AND 8

x7 x8

Here is the ogre shooting gallery. You score 7 points when you shoot a multiple of 7. You score 8 points when you shoot a multiple of 8. If you shoot a multiple of both, you score 15 points! Draw an arrow on each one as you shoot them (as shown).

34　28　77　96　56　44　18　24　70

How many did you find?
Complete the equations.

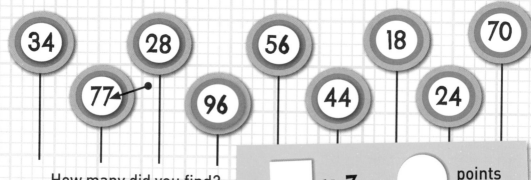

☐ x 7 = ◯ points
multiples of 7

☐ x 8 = ◯ points
multiples of 8

☐ x 15 = ◯ points
multiples of 7 and 8

☐ total score

Remember, if you times any number by 1, the number doesn't change.

OGOR'S PUZZLE TIME

Look at the numbers below. Fill in the shapes that have a multiple of 7 in GREEN. Fill in the shapes that have a multiple of 8 in BROWN. What does the picture reveal?

YOU'RE SMART FOR A HUMAN!

41

MULTIPLY BY 11

Look at the answers below. It's like seeing double!

The 11 times table is easy up to 10.
So let's do those first.
Look at the table, and then cover it up.

11 TIMES TABLE

1 x 11 = 11
2 x 11 = 22
3 x 11 = 33
4 x 11 = 44
5 x 11 = 55
6 x 11 = 66
7 x 11 = 77
8 x 11 = 88
9 x 11 = 99
10 x 11 = 110
11 x 11 = 121
12 x 11 = 132

9 x 11 = ○

7 x 11 = ○

6 x 11 = ○

4 x 11 = ○

3 x 11 = ○

2 x 11 = ○

Now what's this one?
Don't forget, you can switch the numbers around.

10 x 11 = ○

PRACTICE TIME

Now try these.

4 x 11 = ◯   3 x 11 = ◯   7 x 11 = ◯

◯ x 11 = 88   ◯ x 11 = 110

Complete this number pattern.

11 [   ] 33 [   ] 55 [   ] 77 [   ] 99 [   ]

For 11 and 12, here's a tip. You know that 10 x 11 = 110 and 1 x 11 = 11. So if you forget the answer to 11 x 11, add them together!

11 x 11 = | 110 + 11 = 121 |

Using this method, calculate 12 x 11.

10 x 11 = [   ]

2 x 11 = [   ]

12 x 11 = [+   =]

MULTIPLY BY 12

Look at the answers. It's 2, 4, 6, 8, 0 again!

These might be the biggest numbers in the times tables, but you know most of them already. Just switch them around.

12 TIMES TABLE

1 x 12 = 12
2 x 12 = 24
3 x 12 = 36
4 x 12 = 48
5 x 12 = 60
6 x 12 = 72
7 x 12 = 84
8 x 12 = 96
9 x 12 = 108
10 x 12 = 120
11 x 12 = 132
12 x 12 = 144

12 x 2 = ◯

2 x 12 = ◯

12 x 3 = ◯

3 x 12 = ◯

12 x 6 = ◯

6 x 12 = ◯

Now complete these equations.

5 x 12 = ◯

10 x 12 = ◯

8 x 12 = ◯

9 x 12 = ◯

(44)

PRACTICE TIME

Cover up the table, and try these.

10 x 12 = ☐   4 x 12 = ☐   7 x 12 = ☐

☐ x 12 = 60   ☐ x 12 = 24   ☐ x 12 = 132

Complete these.

10 x 12 = ☐

2 x 12 = ☐

Add the answers together to find:

12 x 12 = ☐

Doc the croc is 12 years old. When he is double that age, how old will be?

☐

When he is triple that age, how old will be?

☐

144 is the highest number in the times table grid. Do you know the smallest number? Look on page 13.

Both numbers only appear once.

MULTIPLES OF 11 AND 12

Doc is at Crocodile Rock, the place where he likes to play.
He's made a tower using the rocks that are multiples of 11.
The top one has been done for you. Can you fill in the rest?

123   11   28   88   11

72   132   22   101

66   24   99

Can you do this one, finding the multiples of 12?

120   26   50   60   12

12   102   36   44

72   96   112

46

DOC'S PUZZLE TIME

It's the Crocodile Rock Challenge. To win, Doc is only allowed to swim through the gates with numbers that are multiples of 11 or 12. Help him find his way through them to the finish line.

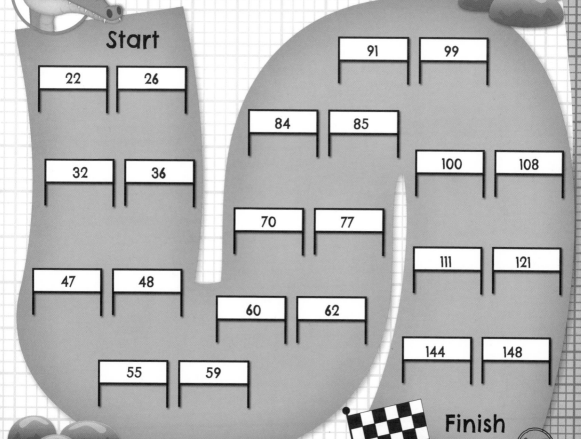

Start

| 22 | 26 |
| 32 | 36 |

91 | 99

84 | 85

70 | 77

| 47 | 48 |

100 | 108

111 | 121

60 | 62

| 55 | 59 |

144 | 148

Finish

47

REMEMBER IT!

Time to test what you remember of your times tables.

If you get stuck, find clues on pages 10 or 13.

1 x 1 =

10 x 1 =

4 x 2 =

8 x 2 =

6 x 3 =

8 x 3 =

3 x 4 =

9 x 4 =

8 x 5 =

6 x 5 =

2 x 6 =

6 x 6 =

8 x 7 =

11 x 7 =

3 x 8 =

6 x 8 =

9 x 9 =

7 x 9 =

3 x 10 =

6 x 10 =

12 x 11 =

9 x 11 =

12 x 12 =

10 x 12 =

$3 \times 10 =$ ☐ $10 \times 10 =$ ☐

$3 \times 100 =$ ☐ $10 \times 100 =$ ☐

$3 \times 1,000 =$ ☐ $10 \times 1,000 =$ ☐

Do you know these?

$0 \times 1 =$ ☐ $0 \times 10 =$ ☐ $0 \times 100 =$ ☐

Complete these two number lines.

11 ☐ 33 ☐ 55 ☐ 77 ☐ 99 ☐

18 27 ☐ 45 ☐ 63 ☐ 81 ☐ 99

Put an arrow going to the multiples of 8. There are three.

19   24   35   60   100

36   48   58   72

PARTITIONING

Doing these in your head is fast!

When you know the times tables, they can help you multiply numbers bigger than 12 without needing to write anything down. All you do is break the equation down into two parts, like this:

12 x 10 = ☐

12 x 5 = ☐

Add the answers. ☐

10 x 11 = ☐

8 x 11 = ☐

Add the answers. ☐

That's how you do these!

12 x 15 = ☐

18 x 11 = ☐

By breaking down equations like this, you can do hard problems in your head. This is "partitioning."

To remember the word, think "PARTS."

PRACTICE TIME

Look once more at the equation 18 x 11.
There are other ways you could break it down.

9 x 11 = ☐

9 x 11 = ☐

Add the answers. ☐

18 x 10 = ☐

18 x 1 = ☐

Add the answers. ☐

Now try the equation 21 x 8 in your head. There are two simple ways to break it down. Which is easiest for you?

20 x 8
1 x 8

Add the answers.

10 x 8
11 x 8

Add the answers.

I'd do it this way.

I'd do it this way.

Write the answer below, then check if you are right.

21 x 8 = ☐

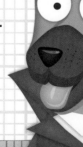

51

SQUARE NUMBERS

When you multiply a number by itself, you get a SQUARE NUMBER.
The number 1 is a square number because 1 multiplied by itself
is 1. The next square number is 4, which is 2 multiplied by 2.

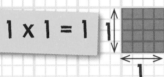

$$1 \times 1 = 1 \qquad 2 \times 2 = 4$$

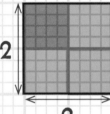

You can see why they are called square
numbers. With two squares on top of two
squares, you get four small squares within
one big one!

A simple way to write this equation is: $2^2 = 4$

The little raised 2
means "squared.".

Can you calculate the
next square number?

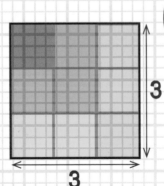

$3^2 = $ ☐

52

PRACTICE TIME

SQUARE NUMBERS

Calculate the other square numbers up to 12 x 12.

$4^2 =$ ☐

$5 \times 5 =$ ☐

$6^2 =$ ☐

$7^2 =$ ☐

$8 \times 8 =$ ☐

$9^2 =$ ☐

$10 \times 10 = 100$

$11^2 =$ ☐

$12 \times 12 =$ ☐

To unlock this safe, Sherlock Bones needs the code. Calculate it for him by finding the square numbers below. Write in the safe code, from low to high.

46   8   12   81   77   6   128

52   90   25   122   49

The safe code is ☐ ☐ ☐

53

FACTORS

Factors are numbers that divide exactly into another number.
All the MULTIPLES in the times tables have FACTORS.
Thinking of factors in pairs can help.

> The grid on page 13 can help you find the factors of a number.

To find the factors of 12, think of what numbers are multiplied together to make 12.

2 x 6   **3 x 4**   **12 x 1**

The factors of 12 are 1, 2, 3, 4, 6, and 12.

Here are the numbers that multiply together to make 9.

9 x 1 = 9   **3 x 3 = 9**

The factors of 9 are ☐ ☐ ☐

Fill in the equations to find the factors of 16.

☐ x 4 = 16   ☐ x 2 = 16   ☐ x 1 = 16

The factors of 16 are ☐ ☐ ☐ ☐ ☐

PRIME NUMBERS

PRIME NUMBERS are special. They can't be divided.

PRIME NUMBER RULES

A prime number has only two factors: **1** and itself.

1 is NOT a prime number. It has only one factor.

2 is the only EVEN prime number.

5 is the only prime number ending in five.

All other prime numbers end in **1, 3, 7,** or **9,** but not all numbers with these endings are prime.

HERE'S HOW TO FIND THEM!

Here are all the numbers up to 20.
Circle the prime numbers, following
the rules above.

1 2 3 4 5 6 7 8 9 10
11 12 13 14 15 16 17 18 19 20

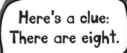

Here's a clue:
There are eight.

USING FACTORS

Using factors is another way to break down difficult problems. If you know the factors of 16, for example, you can break down any equation with 16 as a multiplier.

$16 \times 6 = 8 \times 2 \times 6$ because 8 x 2 is a factor pair of 16

$= 8 \times 12$ because 2 x 6 = 12

$= 96$ We know this from our 12 times table!

Here's another equation. See how you can use factor pairs to keep breaking down an equation into easier parts.

$15 \times 12 = 15 \times 3 \times 4$ 3 x 4 is a factor pair of 12

$= 45 \times 4$ 15 x 3 = 45

$= 45 \times 2 \times 2$ 2 x 2 is a factor pair of 4

$= 90 \times 2$

$= 180$

Only "prime factors," such as 2, 3, 5, and 7, cannot be broken down further.

PRACTICE TIME

Try these equations. Fill in the missing factors, and find the answers.

$31 \times 8 = 31 \times 2 \times 4$
$\quad\quad\quad = 62 \times \boxed{} \times 2$
$\quad\quad\quad = 124 \times 2$
$\quad\quad\quad = \boxed{}$

$15 \times 12 = 3 \times \boxed{} \times 12$
$\quad\quad\quad\quad = 3 \times 60$
$\quad\quad\quad\quad = \boxed{}$

Write down the factor pairs that multiply to make
36

36 x ☐   18 x ☐

12 x ☐   9 x ☐

6 x ☐

The nine factors of 36 are:

☐

Write down the factor pairs that multiply to make
45

1 x ☐   5 x ☐

15 x ☐

The six factors of 45 are:

☐

The largest factor of both 36 and 45 is: ☐

57

REMEMBER IT!

Time to test what you remember of factors and prime numbers.

Write down the eight prime numbers under 20.

Remember the most handy rule: All prime numbers end in 1, 3, 7, and 9, except 2 and 5.

Only two of these numbers are prime numbers. Which ones?

21   23   25   27   29

Which of these is not a factor pair of **35**?

35 x 1   7 x 5   12 x 3

The four factors of **35** are:

Good detectives retrace their steps if they can't find an answer.

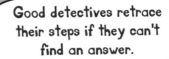

What are the factor pairs of **60**?

| ___ X ___ | ___ X ___ | ___ X ___ |
| ___ X ___ | ___ X ___ | ___ X ___ |

Which of these is not a factor of 60?

1   2   3   4   5   6   10

11   12   15   20   30

Which of these is NOT a prime factor?

2   5   7   9   11

Simplify and solve this equation using factors.

25 x 12 = 25 x ___ X ___

= ___ X ___

= ___

Find the three prime factors that balance these equations.

Clue: Start with any factor pair, and break it down until you get to prime numbers.

___ X ___ X ___	= 30
___ X ___ X ___	= 70
___ X ___ X ___	= 42

WRITTEN MULTIPLICATION

As all good detectives know, when problems get too difficult to calculate in your head, you need to write them down.

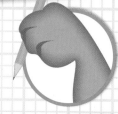

Let's look at the equation
132 x 6
There is no easy way to calculate that in your head, so it's time to get writing.

The trick is to break equations down into easy stages. With each stage, you write down the answer, so that you don't forget it.

We are going to show you two methods for solving hard multiplication equations—the TRADITIONAL METHOD (sometimes called the vertical method) and the GRID METHOD.

I use the traditional method. It never lets me down.

I'm a modern mouse. I use the grid method.

For both methods, you calculate the hundreds, the tens, and the units of a number separately. Then you add up the results. It's the WAY you write the equations down that is different. Look at the equation again.

132 x 6

First, we need to know what each digit in **132** represents.

The **1** is one hundred.

The **3** is thirty (three tens).

The **2** is two (two units).

GRID METHOD

TRADITIONAL METHOD

With the grid method, you draw a grid and put the numbers in the correct columns.

	H Hundreds	T Tens	U Units
x	100	30	2
6			

With the traditional method (or vertical method), you write the equation in columns and rows.

```
H T U
1 3 2
  6 x
_____
```

LET'S START WITH THE GRID METHOD.

GRID METHOD

Ping Ling the Panda will show you how the grid method works. Let's calculate 132 x 6, step by step.

STEP 1

Draw your grid.

X	H Hundreds	T Tens	U Units
Multiplier			

STEP 2

Fill it in with the numbers you want to multiply together.

X	100	30	2
6			

STEP 3

Multiply the hundreds, the tens, and the units by the multiplier.

X	100	30	2
6	600	180	12
	(100 x 6)	(30 x 6)	(2 x 6)

STEP 4

Add each number together to get the answer! If it's hard to add in your head, write it down.

```
 600
 180
  12 +
─────
 792
```

GRID METHOD

Now it's your turn. Calculate the answer to 212 x 4.

STEP 1

Here is the grid filled in. Now multiply the hundreds, tens, and units by the multiplier.

x	200	10	2
4			

STEP 2

Add the numbers together in your head, if you can, and write in the answer to the equation!

212 x 4 = ☐

Now try this one. Don't forget to put the zero into the grid, or you might mix up your hundreds, tens, and units.

108 x 5 = ☐

x	100	0	8
5			

Don't forget, ANY number multiplied by zero makes zero!

AWESOME EFFORT!

PANDA GRIDS

Ping Ling has lots of equations to solve.
Can you help her?

145 x 3 = ▢

x	100	40	5
3			

189 x 2 = ▢

x	100	80	9
2			

106 x 9 = ▢

x	100	0	6
9			

174 x 4 = ▢

x	100	70	4
4			

Having problems adding up in your head? Write the additions down, too!

WRITE YOUR OWN

Time to fill in your own grids, as well as solve the equations!

161 x 6 =

213 x 3 =

121 x 7 =

156 x 5 =

x

x

x

x

READY FOR MORE?

65

MULTIPLYING 1,000s

The grid method works no matter how big the numbers are. All you have do is make the grid bigger, and put the numbers in the right places.

Let's do this equation.

1,230 x 3

First, we need to know what each digit represents.

The **1** is one THOUSAND.

The **2** is two hundred.

The **3** is thirty (three tens).

The **0** is zero (no units).

Because we now have thousands, our grid needs to have four columns.

X	Th Thousands	H Hundreds	T Tens	U Units
Multiplier				

ADD IT UP

Let's put this problem in the grid.

1,230 x 3

x	1,000	200	30	0
3	3,000	600	90	0

3,000 + 600 + 90 + 0 = **3,690**

Here's another equation.

1,521 x 5

x	1,000	500	20	1
5	5,000	2,500	100	5

5,000 + 2,500 + 100 + 5 = **7,605**

> Remember that zeros are really important. If you don't have any tens or units, your answer needs to show it!

DOUBLE-DIGIT MULTIPLIERS

You can use the grid method to multiply by double digits.
You just need to make your grid even bigger!

Let's do this equation.

215 x 21

We know what each digit in **215** represents.

We also know what each digit in **21** represents.

Because we are multiplying a three-digit number
by a two-digit number, our grid needs
to have three columns and two rows, like this.

X	H Hundreds	T Tens	U Units
T Tens			
U Units			

ADD IT UP

Let's put that in the grid.

215 x 21

x	200	10	5	
20	4,000	200	100	4,300
				+
1	2,00	10	5	215
	4,200	+210	+ 105	4,515

Count the zeros in equations like 200 x 20. Three zeros means there are at least three zeros in the answer.

To get the answer, add the columns OR the rows together.

Or you could add the numbers with the same number of digits.

x	200	10	5
20	4,000	200	100
1	200	10	5

4 digits   **4,000**

3 digits   **500**

2 digits   **10**

1 digit   **5**

4,515

See! The answer is the same no matter how you add the numbers.

READY TO TRY?

PANDA GRIDS

Ping Ling has more equations to solve. Can you help her?

117 x 15 = ☐

x	100	10	7
10			
5			

109 x 21 = ☐

x	100	0	9
20			
1			

220 x 34 = ☐

x	200	20	0
30			
4			

Use the spaces for your additions.

PRACTICE TIME

Time to fill in your own grids,
as well as solve the equations!

305 x 22 =

411 x 13 =

181 x 11 =

x

x

x

DIY GRIDS

Time to draw your own grids, as well as solve the equations!

113 x 6 =

180 x 15 =

1317 x 3 =

141 x 34 =

PANDA PUZZLES

Ping Ling is flying to visit her sister. She has some problems to solve before she goes. Can you help?

Ping Ling eats 105 pounds of bamboo a week. How much does she need for a four-week trip?

Ping-ling needs ⬚ lb

Ping Ling is 152 inches from her head to her bottom. She needs a cage three times that length. How long does the cage need to be?

The cage must be ⬚ in

I only travel first-class and expect a luxurious pillow.

FEELING SMART? YOU ARE!

REMEMBER IT!

Calculate the equations here. Draw your own grids.

Time to test what you remember of the grid method.

121 x 5 =

124 x 6 =

208 x 3 =

312 x 7 =

207 x 11 =

309 x 31 =

550 x 12 =

314 x 24 =

Ping Ling weighs 117 pounds. How much would she weigh if she were three times as big?

lb

That would make me ENORMOUS!

TRADITIONAL METHOD

It's ROAR-some when you get the hang of it!

Lionel the lion will show you how the traditional method works. Let's calculate 131 x 3, step by step.

STEP 1
Write the equation in rows and columns. Make sure that the hundreds, tens, and units are in the right columns (headed H, T, and U here).

```
H T U
1 3 1
    3 x
```

STEP 2
Multiply the units first, putting the answer underneath.
1 x 3 = 3

```
1 3 1
    3 x
    3
```

STEP 3
Multiply the tens next, 3 x 3 = 9, then the hundreds, 1 x 3 = 3. Put each answer underneath. And there's your answer: 131 x 3 = 393.

```
1 3 1
    3 x
3 9 3
```

TRADITIONAL METHOD

Now try these equations using this method.

```
  3 2 3
    3 x
┌─────────┐
└─────────┘
```

```
  2 1 2
    4 x
┌─────────┐
└─────────┘
```

Always start with the units.

```
  4 1 3
    2 x
┌─────────┐
└─────────┘
```

```
  2 4 3
    2 x
┌─────────┐
└─────────┘
```

```
  1 3 0
    3 x
┌─────────┐
└─────────┘
```

```
  2 2 1
    4 x
┌─────────┐
└─────────┘
```

If the number has a zero, it's important to write that in the answer.

Can you do this equation? Use the box.

133 x 3

CLAW-SOME!

CARRYING

Don't forget:
U = Units
T = Tens
H = Hundreds
Th = Thousands

With this method, you often have to CARRY because the answer is greater than 10. This means taking numbers over into the next column. Here's how it works.

STEP 1

Write the equation in the same way.

```
H T U
1 1 2
    6 x
```

STEP 2

Multiply the units, 2 x 6 = 12. You know 12 is one ten and two units. Write in the units, and carry the ten to the tens column.

```
1 1 2
    6 x
_____
    2
  1
```

STEP 3

Multiply the tens, 1 x 6 = 6. That's 6 tens. You also have another ten to add from Step 2. So you have 7 tens. Write that in.

```
1 1 2
    6 x
_____
  7 2
  1
```

STEP 4

Multiply the hundreds, 1 x 6 = 6. That's 6 hundreds. Put that in the hundreds column, and there's your answer: 672.

```
1 1 2
    6 x
_____
6 7 2
  1
```

PRACTICE TIME

You can carry tens and hundreds, too, because 10 tens are one hundred, and 10 hundreds are one thousand.

```
Th H T U
    1 5 1
        6 x
    9 0 6
    (3)
```

```
Th H T U
    3 2 1
        4 x
  1,2 8 4
```

300 times 4 is 1,200 (one thousand and two hundreds)

Can you fill in the gaps in these problems?

```
  1 2 0
      7 x
  8 □ 0
    1
```

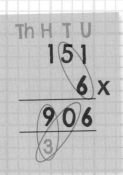

```
  2 0 6
      4 x
  8 □ 4
    2
```

```
  2 7 1
      3 x
  8 1 3
  □
```

CLEVER CARRYING.

Don't forget to add whatever you carry!

LIONEL'S LESSONS

Ready to calculate some lion-sized equations? Remember to write your answers in the correct columns.

I'm here to give you a helping paw, man cub.

Try these ones first.
There is no carrying.

```
  424
   2 x
┌──────┐
│      │
└──────┘
```

```
  203
   3 x
┌──────┐
│      │
└──────┘
```

With these equations, you need to carry the units.
I've done the first one for you.

```
  318
   2 x
──────
  636
```

```
  229
   3 x
┌──────┐
│      │
└──────┘
```

```
  106
   5 x
┌──────┐
│      │
└──────┘
```

BIG numbers are not scary when you tackle them with little bites.

Let's carry some tens to the hundreds column. Again, I've done the first one.

```
  263          141          373
    2 x          4 x          2 x
  526       [        ]    [        ]
 1
```

Ready to carry the hundreds to the thousands column? Again, I've done the first one.

```
   522        1,210        1,301
     4 x          6 x          5 x
 2,088       [        ]    [        ]
```

NICE TRY, MAN CUB!

Big LIONS are pretty scary!

LONG MULTIPLICATION

The traditional method works well when you want to multiply a big number by a big number. Your columns stay the same, but you add more rows.

Be careful with your columns and carrying!

Let's do this equation:

132 x 12

STEP 1

Write out the equation in columns and rows like this. Make sure the digits of both numbers are in the correct columns.

```
Th H  T  U
    1  3  2
       1  2 x
   _____

   _____
```

GOING VERTICAL

STEP 2

Since you are multiplying by 12, get ready to do two stages: 132 x 2 and 132 x 10. Start with the units.

```
Th H  T  U
   1  3  2
      1  2  x
   2  6  4    132 x 2
             132 x 10
```

The zero is the hero! Don't forget it when you multiply the tens.

STEP 3

Now calculate 132 x 10 underneath. You will always have zero units when multiplying by 10, so write the zero units in first.

```
Th  H  T  U
    1  3  2
    1  2  x
    2  6  4   132 x 2
 1, 3  2  0   132 x 10
 1, 5  8  4   132 x 12
```

STEP 4

Add the two answers together.

DON'T DO IT!

The most common mistake people make is to treat the tens as units. Do that, and you end up with the wrong answer.

```
  1 3 2
    1 2 x
  2 6 4
  1 3 2
  3 9 6
```

83

BIG EQUATIONS

Ready to calculate some more lion-sized equations? Remember to write your answers in the correct columns and rows.

A good lion takes it slowly and carefully.

Try this one first. I've done one part for you.

```
Th H T U
   2 1 3
   2 2 x
   _____
              213 x 2
4, 2 6 0      213 x 20
   _____    213 x 22
```

Now try this one. There is no carrying.

```
Th H T U
   3 2 0
   3 1 x
   _____
   _____     320 x 1
             320 x 30
   _____     320 x 30
```

PRACTICE TIME

Here are some practice questions. Try them.

41		23		52	
22 x		21 x		13 x	
⬜	41 x 2	⬜	23 x 1	⬜	52 x 3
	41 x 20		23 x 20		52 x 10
⬜	41 x 22	⬜	23 x 21	⬜	52 x 13

With long multiplication, you can carry. Here's an example.

Th H T U

$$\begin{array}{r} 213 \\ 17 \times \\ \hline 1,491 \\ 2,130 \\ \hline 3,621 \\ \hline \end{array}$$

213 x 7
213 x 10
213 x 17

If you want to challenge yourself, try this.

Th H T U

$$\begin{array}{r} 561 \\ 13 \times \\ \hline \end{array}$$

561 x 3
561 x 10
561 x 13

You can do it!

REMEMBER IT!

Time to test what you remember of the two methods of long multiplication.

Calculate the equations using the grid method here.

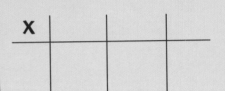

x

181 x 5 =

124 x 6 =

207 x 15 =

261 x 24 =

Calculate the equations here using the traditional method.

$$323 \\ 3 \times$$

323 x 3 =

209 x 5 =

38 x 21 =

613 x 13 =

Lionel weighs 172 pounds. How much would he weigh if he were three times as big?

lb

THE LONG MULTIPLICATION TEST

Find the answers to these equations using whichever method you like. Don't forget factors (page 56) and partitioning (page 50). They may be quicker. Think about how to calculate each equation before you start.

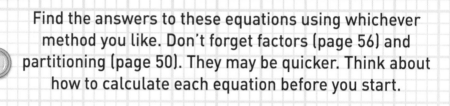

42 x 3 =

18 x 11 =

68 x 5 =

95 x 9 =

215 x 6 =

219 x 4 =

307 x 13 =

612 x 19 =

511 x 18 =

820 x 25 =

Use this page to calculate problems.

TEST TIME

Check your answers on page 96.

Don't worry if you get a few wrong. Even great detectives make mistakes!

89

THE BIG TEST

It's time to test what you have learned.

Here's a part of the times table grid.
Fill in the missing numbers.

	6	7	8	9	10	11	12
6			48			66	
7	42				70		
8				72			96
9		63				99	
10	60						120
11					110		
12		84		108		132	

Find the question with the different answer.

What is … ?
six times eight
the product of eight and six
the equation of six and eight
6 x 8
8 multiplied by 6
six groups of eight

Help Doc build a rock tower
with multiples of 9.

22

45   108   79   72   54

66   25   28   36   90

Find the square numbers to crack the safe code (low to high).

46   99   8   50   4   72

16   81

The safe code is ☐ ☐ ☐

Only two of these numbers are NOT prime numbers. Which ones?

3   7   28   19   33   31   13

Write down the factor pairs of 56.

☐ X ☐   ☐ X ☐

☐ X ☐   ☐ X ☐

Use whichever method you like for these long multiplication equations.

243 x 5 = ☐

18 x 12 = ☐

714 x 6 = ☐

250 x 6 = ☐

242 x 20 = ☐

391 x 17 = ☐

52 x 22 = ☐

1,241 x 3 = ☐

SHERLOCK'S ANSWERS

Page 8
STINGERS: 8, 10, 12
STINKERS: 9, 12
6 and 12 are both

Page 9
The gaps are 14, 18, 22
and 15, 21, 27, 33

Page 11
7 x 6 and 6 x 7 = 42

Page 12
9 x 8 = 72   6 x 3 = 18
12 x 11 = 132   7 x 1 = 7
10 x 6 = 60   12 x 2 = 24

Page 14
2 x 2 = 4   5 x 2 = 10
7 x 2 = 14   10 x 2 = 20
12 x 2 = 24   1 x 2 = 2

Page 15
The gaps are 4, 14, 24
and 22, 12, 2

Pip and his Pa have
caught 8 x 2 = 16 fish.

Page 16
4 x 4 = 16   11 x 4 = 44
9 x 4 = 36   2 x 4 = 8
8 x 4 = 32   5 x 4 = 20

Page 17
7 x 4 = 28   9 x 4 = 36
12 x 4 = 48   10 x 4 = 40
3 x 4 = 12

The gaps are 12, 28, 44.
52 comes after 48.

Page 18
7 is not a multiple of 2.
22 is not a multiple of 4.

Page 19
Pip wins, 14 points to
12 points!

There are 5 multiples
of 2: 20, 6, 44, 16, 28.
There are 4 multiples
of 4: 20, 44, 16, 28.

Page 20
1 x 10 = 10   8 x 10 = 80
11 x 10 = 110   2 x 10 = 20
4 x 10 = 40   7 x 10 = 70
13 x 10 = 130

Page 21
12 x 10 = 120   6 x 10 = 60
Coco has 50 pearls.
The gaps are 20, 40, 60,
80, 100, 120
and 130, 150, 170.

Page 22
5 x 5 = 25   3 x 5 = 15
7 x 5 = 35   9 x 5 = 45
8 x 5 = 40   4 x 5 = 20
13 x 5 = 65

Page 23
6 x 5 = 30   2 x 5 = 10
10 x 5 = 50   9 x 5 = 45
11 x 5 = 55   5 x 5 = 25

Coco visits 5 x 7 = 35
anemones.

Coco takes 5 x 3 = 15
minutes.

The gaps are 30, 45.

Page 24
The other multiples of 5
are 15, 300, 50, 65, 35, 95,
70, 110.

The multiples of 10 are
300, 50, 70, 110, 80.

202 x 5 = 101<u>0</u> 55 x 5 = 27<u>5</u>

Page 25
4 orange shells x 5 = 20
4 purple shells x 10 = 40
Total 60 points

Page 27

	Th	H	T	U
6 x 10 =			6	0
6 x 100 =		6	0	0
6 x 1,000 =	6	0	0	0
16 x 100 =	1	6	0	0

Page 28
3 x 3 = 9   8 x 3 = 24
9 x 3 = 27   12 x 3 = 36

Page 29
23 x 3 = ODD
18 x 3 = EVEN

Flip takes 5 leaps to
cover 15 laps.

Page 30
2 x 6 = 12   4 x 6 = 24
5 x 6 = 30   11 x 6 = 66
7 x 3 = ㉑   7 x 3 = ㉑
7 x 6 = ㉑ + ㉑ = 42

Page 31

3 x 6 = 18   8 x 6 = 48
12 x 6 = 72   4 x 6 = 24
7 x 6 = 42   9 x 6 = 54

In six days, Flip eats
6 x 6 = 36 bugs.
In seven days, Flip eats
6 x 7 = 42 bugs.
The gaps are 12, 24, 36, 48.

Page 32

9 x 9 = 81

Page 33

3 x 9 = 27   2 x 9 = 18
11 x 9 = 99   10 x 9 = 90
1 x 9 = 9   6 x 9 = 54

4 x 9 = 36

Page 34

The special lily pad is 18

Page 35

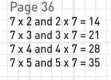

36 is a multiple of 3, 6 & 9.

Page 36

7 x 2 and 2 x 7 = 14
7 x 3 and 3 x 7 = 21
7 x 4 and 4 x 7 = 28
7 x 5 and 5 x 7 = 35

Page 37

6 x 7 = 42   7 x 7 = 49
8 x 7 = 56
The gaps are 14, 35,
49, 70.

Page 38

5 x 8 = 40   2 x 8 = 16
9 x 8 = 72

3 x 4 = ⑫ 3 x 4 = ⑫
3 x 8 = ⑫ + ⑫ = 24

Page 39

6 x 8 = 48   7 x 8 = 56
12 x 8 = 96   3 x 8 = 24
11 x 8 = 88   8 x 8 = 64

The gaps are 24, 32, 40, 48,
56, 64, 72, 80.

Ogor has 8 x 2 = 16 holes.
He needs 8 x 8 = 64
pennies.

Page 40

The multiples of 7 are

77   28   56   70

The multiples of 8 are

96   56   24

4 x 7 = 28 points
3 x 8 = 24 points
1 x 15 = 15 points
Total score 67

Page 41

Page 42

9 x 11 = 99   7 x 11 = 77
6 x 11 = 66   4 x 11 = 44
3 x 11 = 33   2 x 11 = 22
10 x 11 = 110

Page 43

4 x 11 = 44   3 x 11 = 33
7 x 11 = 77   8 x 11 = 88
10 x 11 = 110

The gaps are 22, 44, 66,
88, 110.
10 x 11 = 110
2 x 11 = 22
12 x 11 = 110 + 22 = 132

Page 44

12 x 2 and 2 x 12 = 24
12 x 3 and 3 x 12 = 36
12 x 6 and 6 x 12 = 72
5 x 12 = 60   10 x 12 = 120
8 x 12 = 96   9 x 12 = 108

Page 45

10 x 12 = 120
4 x 12 = 48
7 x 12 = 84
5 x 12 = 60
2 x 12 = 24
11 x 12 = 132

10 x 12 = 120
2 x 12 = 24
12 x 12 = 144

Double (12 x 2): Doc
will be 24 years old.

Triple (12 x 3): Doc
will be 36 years old.

The smallest number
is 1.

Page 46

```
      11
   22    66
 88   99   132
```

The order doesn't
matter.

```
      12
   36    60
 72   96   120
```

Page 47

The right gates are:
22, 36, 48, 55, 60,
77, 84, 99, 108,
121, 144.

ANSWERS

Page 48
1 x 1 = 1   8 x 7 = 56
10 x 1 = 10   11 x 7 = 77
4 x 2 = 8   3 x 8 = 24
8 x 2 = 16   6 x 8 = 48
6 x 3 = 18   9 x 9 = 81
8 x 3 = 24   7 x 9 = 63
3 x 4 = 12   3 x 10 = 30
9 x 4 = 36   6 x 10 = 60
8 x 5 = 40   12 x 11 = 132
6 x 5 = 30   9 x 11 = 99
2 x 6 = 12   12 x 12 = 144
6 x 6 = 36   10 x 12 = 120

Page 49
3 x 10 = 30
3 x 100 = 300
3 x 1,000 = 3,000
10 x 10 = 100
10 x 100 = 1,000
10 x 1,000 = 10,000
0 x 1 = 0
0 x 10 = 0
0 x 100 = 0

The gaps are
22, 44, 66, 88, 110
and 36, 54, 72, 90.

The multiples of 8 are

24   48   72

Page 50
12 x 10 = 120
12 x 5 = 60 +
12 x 15 = 180

10 x 11 = 110
 8 x 11 = 88 +
18 x 11 = 198

Page 51
 9 x 11 = 99
 9 x 11 = 99 +
18 x 11 = 198

18 x 10 = 180
18 x 1 = 18 +
18 x 11 = 198

20 x 8 = 160
 1 x 8 = 8 +
21 x 8 = 168

10 x 8 = 80
11 x 8 = 88 +
21 x 8 = 168

Page 52
$3^2 = 9$

Page 53
$4^2 = 16$ 5 x 5 = 25
$6^2 = 36$ $7^2 = 49$
8 x 8 = 64 $9^2 = 81$
10 x 10 = 100 $11^2 = 121$
12 x 12 = 144

The safe code is
25, 49, 81.

Page 54
The factors of 9 are
1, 3, 9.
4 x 4 = 16
8 x 2 = 16
16 x 1 = 16
The factors of 16 are
1, 2, 4, 8, 16.

Page 55
The prime numbers are
2, 3, 5, 7, 11, 13, 17, 19.

Page 57
31 x 8 = 62 x 2 x 2
        = 248
15 x 12 = 3 x 5 x 12
        = 180

The factor pairs of 36 are
36 x 1   18 x 2   12 x 3
   9 x 4   6 x 6.
The factors of 36 are
1, 2, 3, 4, 6, 9, 12, 18, 36.

The factor pairs of 45 are
1 x 45   5 x 9   15 x 3.
The factors of 45 are
1, 3, 5, 9, 15, 45.

The largest factor of
both 36 and 45 is 9.

Page 58
The eight prime
numbers under 20 are
2, 3, 5, 7, 11, 13, 17, 19.

23 and 29 are the two
prime numbers.

12 x 3 is not a factor
pair of 35.

The four factors of
35 are 1, 5, 7, 35.

Page 59
The factor pairs of 60 are
1 x 60   2 x 30   3 x 20
4 x 15   5 x 12   6 x 10.
11 is not a factor of 60.

9 is not a prime factor.

There are two correct
answers:
25 x 12 = 25 x 4 x 3
        = 100 x 3
        = 300
OR
25 x 12 = 25 x 2 x 6
        = 50 x 6
        = 300

2 x 3 x 5 = 30
2 x 5 x 7 = 70
2 x 3 x 7 = 42

Page 63
212 x 4 = 800 + 40 + 8 = 848
108 x 5 = 500 + 0 + 40 = 540

Page 64
145 x 3 = 300 + 120 + 15 = 435
189 x 2 = 200 + 160 + 18 = 378
106 x 9 = 900 + 0 + 54 = 954
174 x 4 = 400 + 280 + 16 = 696

ANSWERS

Page 65
161 x 6 = 600 + 360 + 6 = 966
213 x 3 = 600 + 30 + 9 = 639
121 x 7 = 700 + 140 + 7 = 847
156 x 5 = 500 + 250 + 30 = 780

Page 70
117 x 15 = 1,755
(1,000 + 100 + 70) + (500 + 50 + 35)
109 x 21 = 2,289
(2,000 + 0 + 180) + (100 + 0 + 9)
220 x 34 = 7,480
(6,000 + 600 + 0) + (800 + 80 + 0)

Page 71
305 x 22 = 6,710
(6,000 + 0 + 100) + (600 + 0 + 10)
411 x 13 = 5,343
(4,000 + 100 + 10) + (1,200 + 30 + 3)
181 x 11 = 1,991
(1,000 + 800 + 10) + (100 + 80 + 1)

Page 72
113 x 6 = 678
(600 + 60 + 18)
180 x 15 = 2,700
(1,000 + 800 + 0) + (500 + 400 + 0)
1,317 x 3 = 3,951
(3,000 + 900 + 30 + 21)
141 x 34 = 4,794
(3,000 + 1,200 + 30) + (400 + 160 + 4)

Page 73
Ping Ling needs 420 lb.

The cage must be 456 in.

Page 74
121 x 5 = 500 + 100 + 5 = 605
124 x 6 = 600 + 120 + 24 = 744
208 x 3 = 600 + 0 + 24 = 624
312 x 7 = 2,100 + 70 + 14 = 2,184

Page 75
207 x 11 = 2,277
(2,000 + 0 + 70) + (200 + 0 + 7)
309 x 31 = 9,579
(9,000 + 0 + 270) + (300 + 0 + 9)
550 x 12 = 6,600
(5,000 + 500 + 0) + (1,000 + 100 + 0)
314 x 24 = 7,536
(6,000 + 200 + 80) + (1,200 + 40 + 16)

Ping Ling would be 351 lb.

Page 77
```
  323          212
    3 x          4 x
  969          848

  413          243
    2 x          2 x
  826          486

  130          221
    3 x          4 x
  390          884

               133
                 3 x
               399
```

Page 79
```
  120
    7 x
  840
   1

  206          271
    4 x          3 x
  824          813
   2            2
```

Page 80
```
  424          203
    2 x          3 x
  848          609

  229          106
    3 x          5 x
  687          530
   2            3
```

Page 81
```
  141          373
    4 x          2 x
  564          746
   1            1

1,210        1,301
    6 x          5 x
7,260        6,505
   1            1
```

95

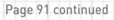

ANSWERS

Page 84

```
  213          320
  22 x         31 x
 426          320
4,260        9,600
4,686        9,920
```

Page 85

```
  41           23
  22 x         21 x
  82           23
 820          460
 902          483


  52          561
  13 x         13 x
 156         1,683
 520         5,610
 676         7,293
```

Page 86

181 x 5 = 905
(500 +400 + 5)
124 x 6 = 744
(600 +120 + 24)
207 x 15 = 3,105
(2,000 + 0 + 70) + (1,000 + 0 + 35)
261 x 24 = 6,264
(4,000 + 1,200 + 20) + (800 + 240 + 4)

Page 87

```
 323          209
   3 x          5 x
 969        1,045
```

Page 87 continued

```
  38          613
  21 x         13 x
  38        1,839
 760        6,130
 798        7,969
```

Lionel would weigh 516 lb.

Page 88

42 x 3 = 126
18 x 11 = 198
68 x 5 = 340
95 x 9 = 855
215 x 6 = 1,290
219 x 4 = 876
307 x 13 = 3,991
612 x 19 = 11,628
511 x 18 = 9,198
820 x 25 = 20,500

Page 90

The equation of six and eight means 6 + 8 = 14. All the rest are the same as 6 x 8 or 8 x 6 = 48.

For the grid, check your answers on page 13.

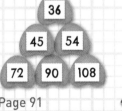

```
        36
     45    54
   72   90   108
```

Page 91

The safe code is 4, 16, 81.

28 and 33 are not prime numbers.

Page 91 continued

The factor pairs of 56 are
1 x 56   2 x 28
4 x 14   7 x 8

The recommended methods of calculation come after the equation.

243 x 5 = 1,215 (grid or traditional)

18 x 12 = 216 (partitioning, 18 x 10 added to 18 x 2)

714 x 6 = 4,284 (grid or traditional)

250 x 6 = 1,500 (in your head using factors: 250 x 2 x 3)

242 x 20 = 4,840 (in your head using factors, 242 x 2 x 10)

391 x 17 = 6,647 (grid or traditional)

52 x 22 = 1,144 (partitioning, 52 x 20 added to 52 x 2)

1,241 x 3 = 3,723 (grid or traditional)